Going to the Dentist

P9-BAU-053

Bath · New York · Singapore · Hong Kong · Cologne · Delhi
Melbourne · Amsterdam · Johannesburg · Auckland · Shenzhen

Page 7

Page 10-11

Page 14

Page 16-17

Page 17

Page 21

Page 24

Page 28-29

Page 29

How to use this book

Read the story, all about Jacob
and his first visit to the dentist.

Look at each picture in the story closely.
You may be asked to find or count things
in a scene and place a sticker on the page.

Try each activity as you go along, or read
the story first, then go back and do the
activities. The answers are at the bottom
of each activity page.

Some pictures will need stickers to finish
the scenes or activities. Any leftover
stickers can be used to decorate your
certificate or your things.

Today, Jacob and his mom are going to the dentist. It will be Jacob's first visit.

Find these things in the kitchen.

Mom pours a glass of milk for Jacob. "Milk helps to make your teeth strong," she says.

Can you find 4 blue things in the picture?

Now put Jacob's teddy bear sticker here.

After breakfast, Mom helps Jacob do
a really good job brushing his teeth. He has
a blue toothbrush and stripy toothpaste.

Can you spot five differences between these two pictures?

Answer

At the dentist's, Jacob and his mom take a seat in the waiting room. Jacob feels a little nervous.

Can you find these things in the picture?

Then he sees his friend, Noah, coming out of the dentist's exam room.

"Look!" says Noah. "The dentist gave me a smiley sticker for having such clean teeth!" Jacob hopes he'll get a smiley sticker, too.

Look at Noah's sticker in the picture on the opposite page. Can you find a sticker below that matches it exactly?

Answer

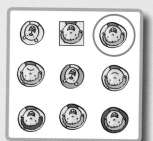

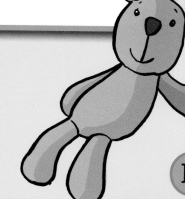

Point to all the things on this page that begin with the letter "t."

Answer

Tooth fairy, toothpaste, tooth, toothbrush, and teddy all begin with the letter "t."

15

"Hello, Jacob!" says the dentist. "My name is Dr. Bright. Come and sit in my special chair."

Can you find these things in the picture?

The dentist presses a button and the chair goes up and slowly tips backward!

Find 2 stickers to finish the picture.

Find the calendar sticker.

Dr. Bright shows Jacob the little mirror and probe he will use to check his teeth.

The nurse gives Jacob special glasses to wear. "These will protect your eyes," she says.

Which of these things would you find at the dentist's?

Answer

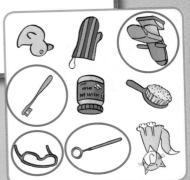

"Now, open wide please, Jacob!" says Dr. Bright.
Jacob opens his mouth as wide as he can.

Can you find these things in the picture?

Dr. Bright counts Jacob's teeth. He uses the mirror to see right inside Jacob's mouth.

Place the sticker of the cat picture here.

"Good job, Jacob. Your teeth are very clean!" says Dr. Bright. "Now, rinse out your mouth!"

The nurse hands Jacob a glass of pink mouthwash. Jacob sloshes it around in his mouth and spits it into a special sink.

Look carefully at the picture below. Point to where each piece goes in the jigsaw puzzle.

d.

Answer

a.

b.

c.

"Brush your teeth twice a day for two minutes," says Dr. Bright. "And don't eat too many sugary treats," says the nurse.

She gives Jacob a smiley face sticker.
"It's just like Noah's!" says Jacob.

Can you help Jacob to find the healthy snack? Follow the tangled lines to the apple.

a.

b.

c.

Answer Line "c." leads to the apple.

Mom thanks the dentist. "Good-bye, Jacob. See you again in six months!" he says.

Point to the thing that is different in each row.

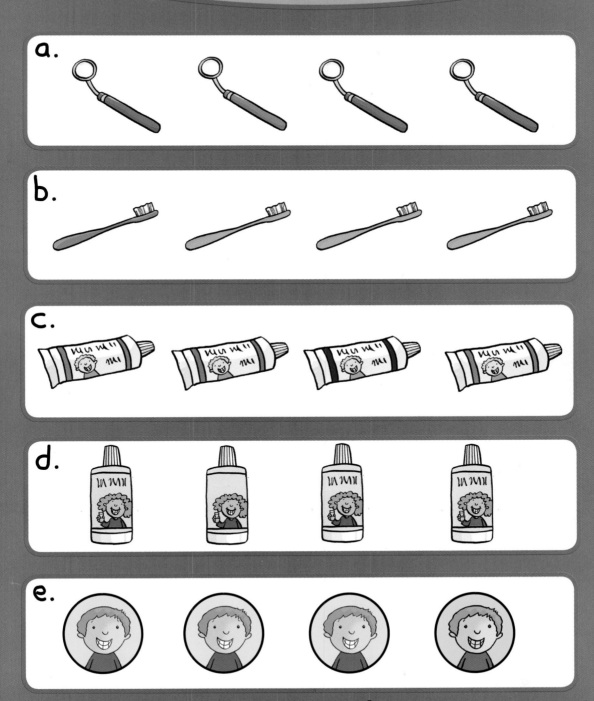

a.

b.

c.

d.

e.

Back at home, Jacob pretends to be a dentist. His stuffed animals are his patients.

Can you find these things in Jacob's room?

"Good job, Teddy! Your teeth look great!" he says.
"I can see you don't eat too much candy."

At bedtime, Jacob brushes his teeth really well.
"I like having clean teeth," he tells Teddy.